designs COLORING BOOK

> *Colors; in paste or crayon, pencil; always a thrill. To this I love to hold a handful of many-colored pencils and ope. hand to see them lying loose upon my palm, in the light.*
>
> —Frank Lloyd ....ght

The architect and designer Frank Lloyd Wright (American, 1867–1959) single-handedly changed how Americans thought about houses, insisting on more light, less clutter, freer movement from room to room, and the honesty of good materials displaying their natural color and texture. Driven by the belief that the places people live and the things they use every day should reflect the surrounding landscape—he called this an "organic" way of creating new objects—Wright designed many of the furnishings for his famous houses, churches, and commercial buildings. He gave special attention to windows and loved to decorate them with art glass designs.

You'll find twenty-two designs in this coloring book, adapted from magazine covers, carpets, tiles, windows, and other Wright projects. They are shown as small pictures inside the front and back covers. You'll notice that the artist used many straight lines to make patterns, which sometimes look like familiar things—a bowl of fruit, flags, plants and flowers. When you color in a picture, you might want to try to make something close to the original, or you might decide to use colors that are quite different.

The last page of this book is blank so that you can draw and color your own picture. Use a ruler and a compass and see if you can make a picture that looks like something Frank Lloyd Wright might have done.

Pomegranate kids™

1. Adaptation of Frank Lloyd Wright (American, 1867–1959), Carpet design (project), Arthur B. Heurtley House, Oak Park, Illinois, 1902

2. Adaptation of Frank Lloyd Wright (American, 1867–1959), Tile/frieze design (project), Avery Coonley House, Riverside, Illinois, 1907

3. Adaptation of Frank Lloyd Wright (American, 1867–1959), *Liberty* magazine cover (project), *March Balloons*, 1927

4. Adaptation of Frank Lloyd Wright (American, 1867–1959), Art glass triptych windows, Coonley Playhouse, Riverside, Illinois, 1912

5. Adaptation of Frank Lloyd Wright (American, 1867–1959), *Liberty* magazine cover (project), *Desert Triangles*, 1927

6. Adaptation of Frank Lloyd Wright (American, 1867–1959), *Waterlilies* art glass screen (project), 1895

7. Adaptation of Frank Lloyd Wright (American, 1867–1959), Tile/frieze design (project), Avery Coonley House, Riverside, Illinois, 1907

8. Adaptation of Frank Lloyd Wright (American, 1867–1959), *Liberty* magazine cover (project), *Bird in the Cage*, 1927

9. Adaptation of Frank Lloyd Wright (American, 1867–1959), Mural detail, *City by the Sea*, Music Pavilion, Taliesin West, Scottsdale, Arizona, 1956

10. Adaptation of Frank Lloyd Wright (American, 1867–1959), *Liberty* magazine cover detail (project), *Saguaro Forms and Cactus Flowers*, 1927

11. Adaptation of Frank Lloyd Wright (American, 1867–1959), Mural detail, Imperial Hotel, Tokyo, Japan, 1913–1922

12. Adaptation of Frank Lloyd Wright (American, 1867–1959), *Liberty* magazine cover, *Flags*, 1927

13. Adaptation of Frank Lloyd Wright (American, 1867–1959), Fretwork grille detail for front door, Chauncey L. Williams House, River Forest, Illinois, 1895

14. Adaptation of Frank Lloyd Wright (American, 1867–1959), *Liberty* magazine cover (project), *May Basket*, 1927

15. Adaptation of Frank Lloyd Wright (American, 1867–1959), Carpet design, Avery Coonley House, Riverside, Illinois, 1907

16. Adaptation of Frank Lloyd Wright (American, 1867–1959), *Liberty* magazine cover detail (project), *December Gifts*, 1927

17. Adaptation of Frank Lloyd Wright (American, 1867–1959), Tile/frieze design (project), Avery Coonley House, Riverside, Illinois, 1907

18. Adaptation of Frank Lloyd Wright (American, 1867–1959), *Liberty* magazine cover (project), *Frozen Spheres*, 1927

19. Adaptation of Frank Lloyd Wright (American, 1867–1959), *Liberty* magazine cover (project), *Jewelry Shop Window*, 1927

20. Adaptation of Frank Lloyd Wright (American, 1867–1959), Fretwork grille detail for front door, Nathan Moore House, Oak Park, Illinois, 1923

21. Adaptation of Frank Lloyd Wright (American, 1867–1959), *Liberty* magazine cover detail (project), *Old-Fashioned Window*, 1927

22. Adaptation of Frank Lloyd Wright (American, 1867–1959), Metal altar screen detail, Annunciation Greek Orthodox Church, Wauwatosa, Wisconsin, 1956

© 2009 THE FRANK LLOYD WRIGHT FOUNDATION
TALIESIN WEST, SCOTTSDALE, ARIZONA
ALL RIGHTS RESERVED

This Frank Lloyd Wright Collection® product is authorized by the Frank Lloyd Wright Foundation, Taliesin West, Scottsdale, Arizona. A portion of the sales of this product supports the conservation and education programs of the foundation. www.franklloydwright.org

Pomegranate Communications, Inc.
Box 808022, Petaluma CA 94975
800 227 1428
www.pomegranate.com

Pomegranate Europe Ltd.
Unit 1, Heathcote Business Centre, Hurlbutt Road
Warwick, Warwickshire CV34 6TD, UK
[+44] 0 1926 430111
sales@pomeurope.co.uk

Catalog No. CB109

Designed by Shannon Lemme

Printed in Korea

This product is in compliance with the Consumer Product Safety Improvement Act of 2008 (CPSIA). A General Conformity Certificate concerning Pomegranate's compliance with the CPSIA is available on our website at www.pomegranate.com, or by request at 800 227 1428.

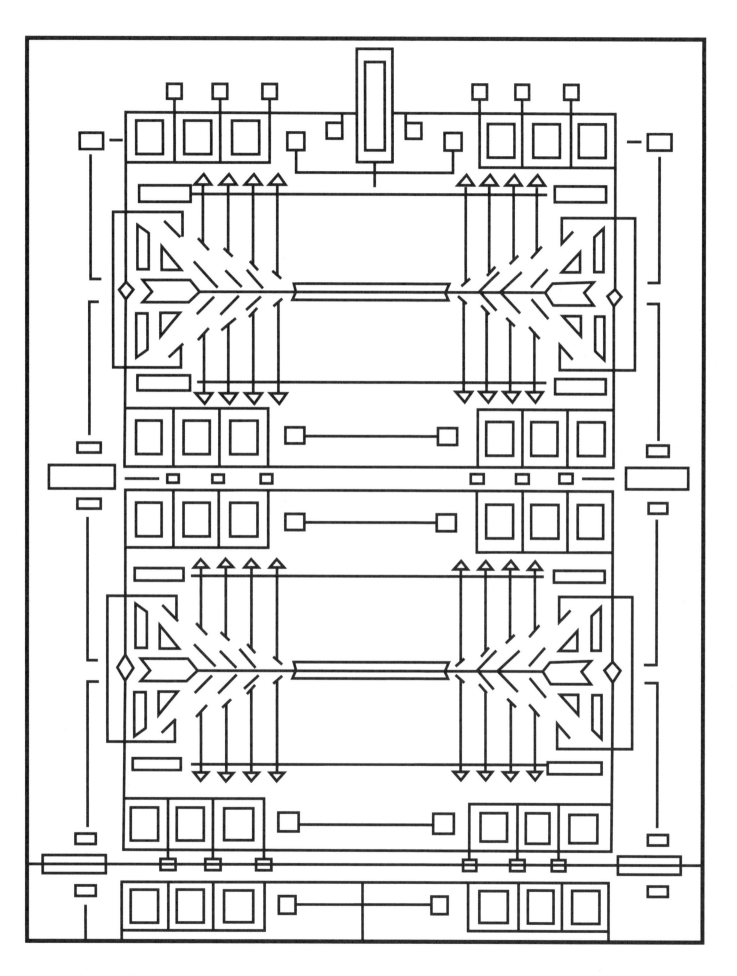

1. Adaptation of Frank Lloyd Wright (American, 1867–1959), Carpet design (project), Arthur B. Heurtley House, Oak Park, Illinois, 1902

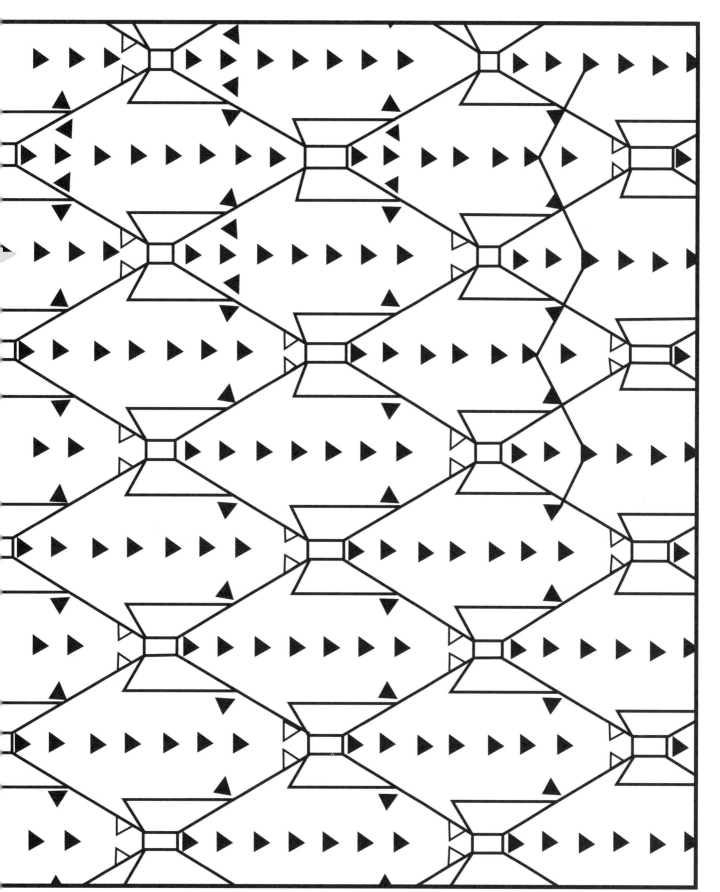

2. Adaptation of Frank Lloyd Wright (American, 1867–1959), Tile/frieze design (project), Avery Coonley House, Riverside, Illinois, 1907

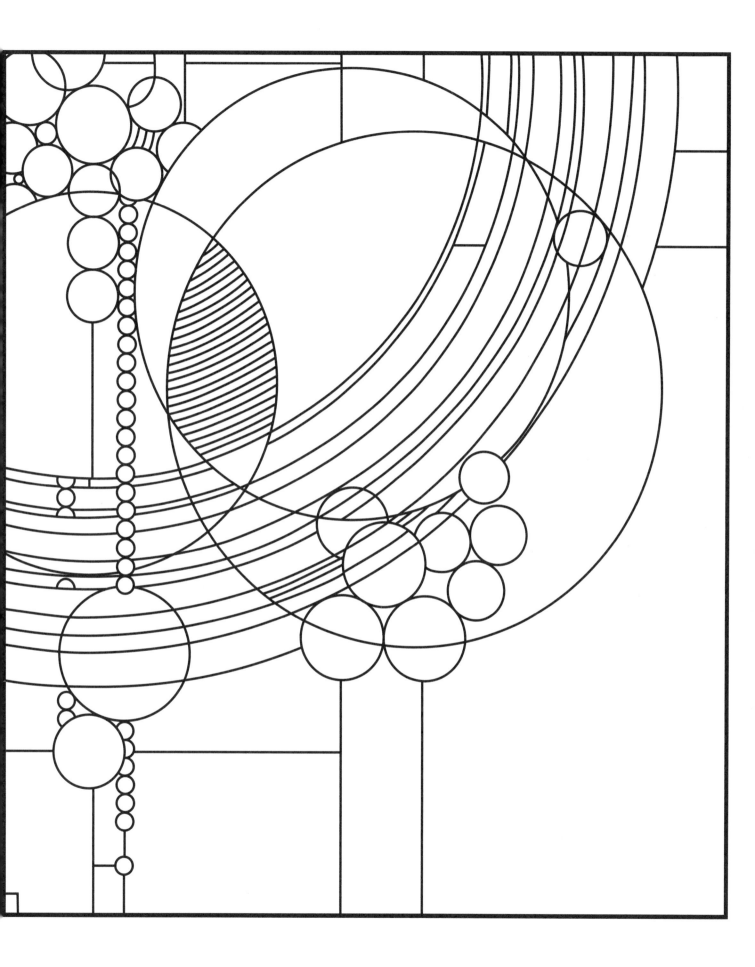

3. Adaptation of Frank Lloyd Wright (American, 1867–1959), *Liberty* magazine cover (project), *March Balloons*, 1927

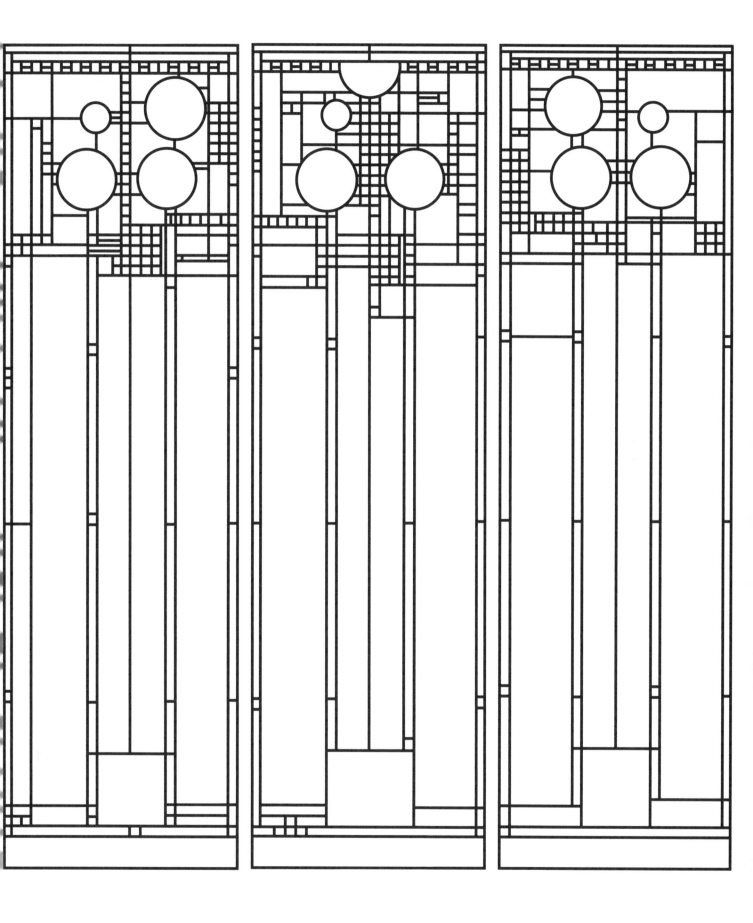

4. Adaptation of Frank Lloyd Wright (American, 1867–1959), Art glass triptych windows, Coonley Playhouse, Riverside, Illinois, 1912

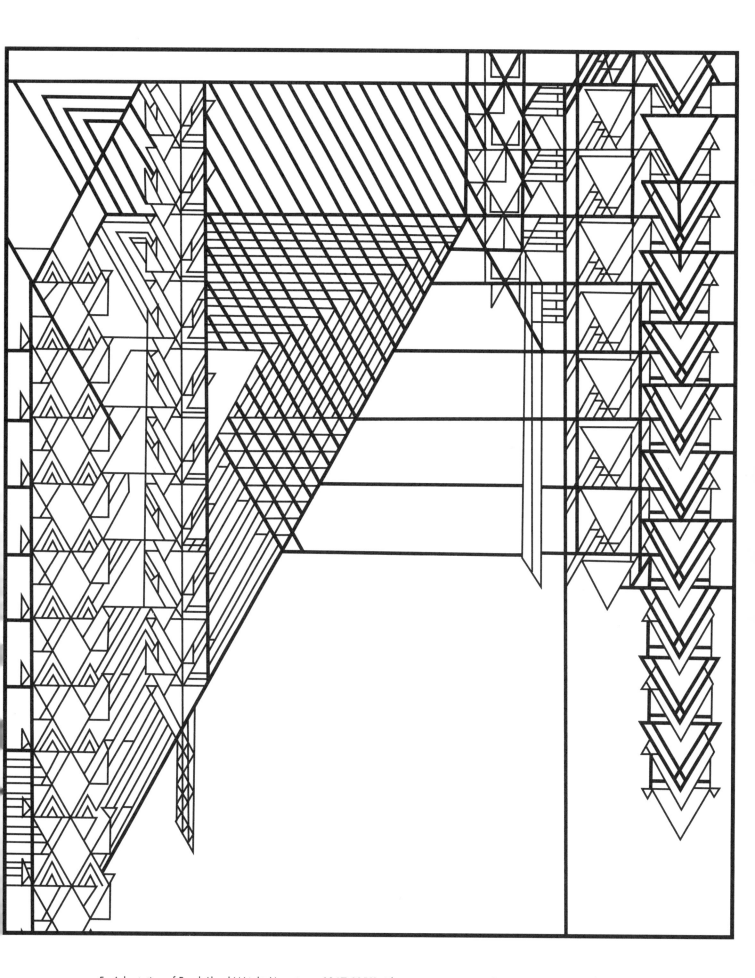

5. Adaptation of Frank Lloyd Wright (American, 1867–1959), *Liberty* magazine cover (project), *Desert Triangles,* 1927

6. Adaptation of Frank Lloyd Wright (American, 1867–1959), *Waterlilies* art glass screen (project), 1895

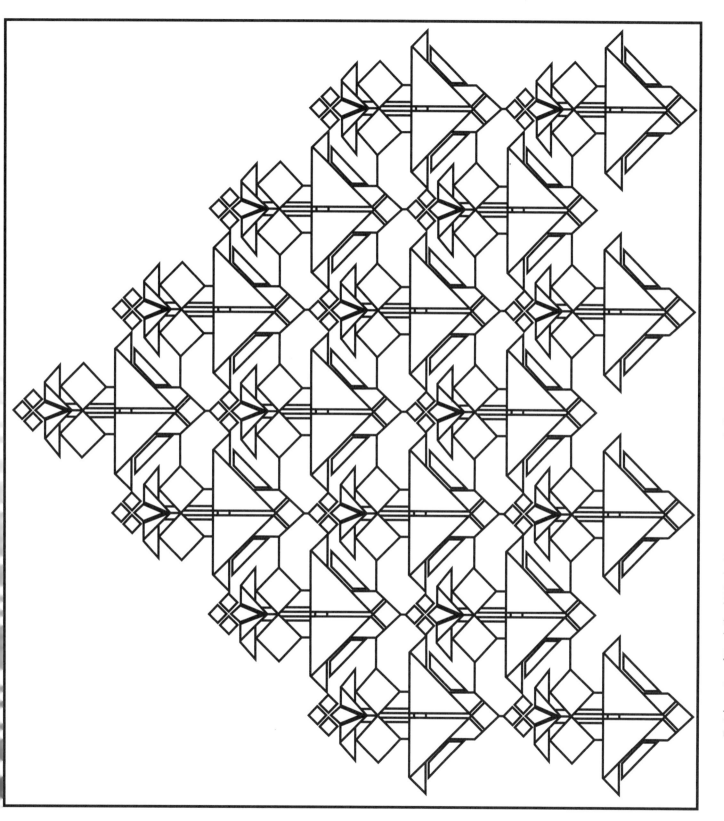

7. Adaptation of Frank Lloyd Wright (American, 1867–1959), Tile/frieze design (project), Avery Coonley House, Riverside, Illinois, 1907

8. Adaptation of Frank Lloyd Wright (American, 1867–1959), *Liberty* magazine cover (project), *Bird in the Cage,* 1927

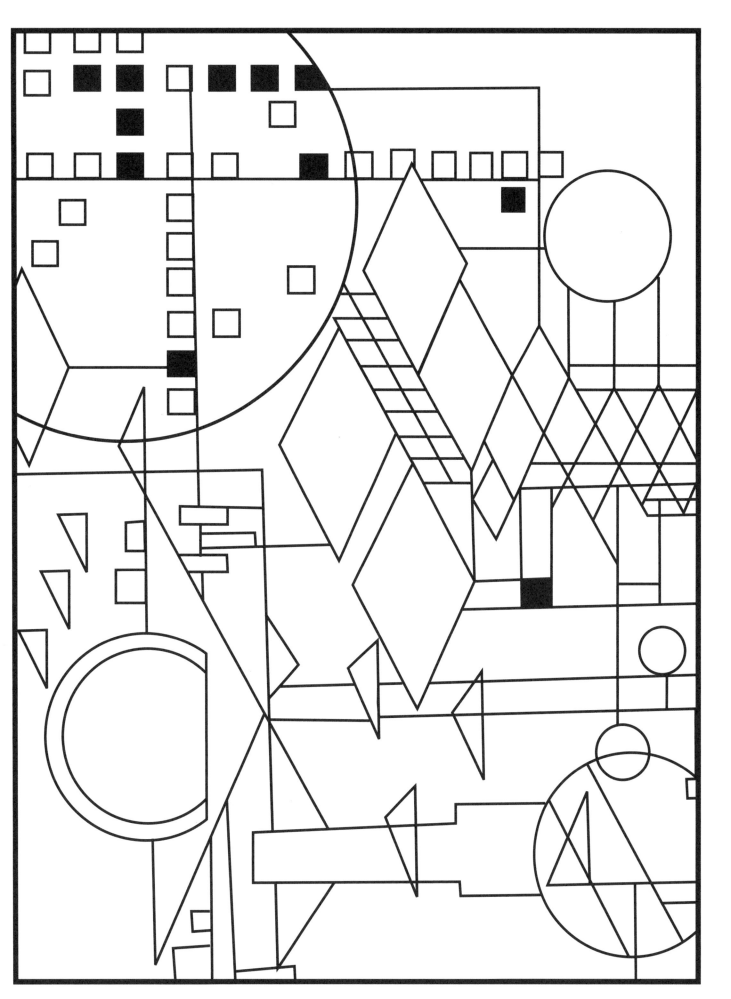

9. Adaptation of Frank Lloyd Wright (American, 1867–1959), Mural detail, *City by the Sea*, Music Pavilion, Taliesin West, Scottsdale, Arizona, 1956

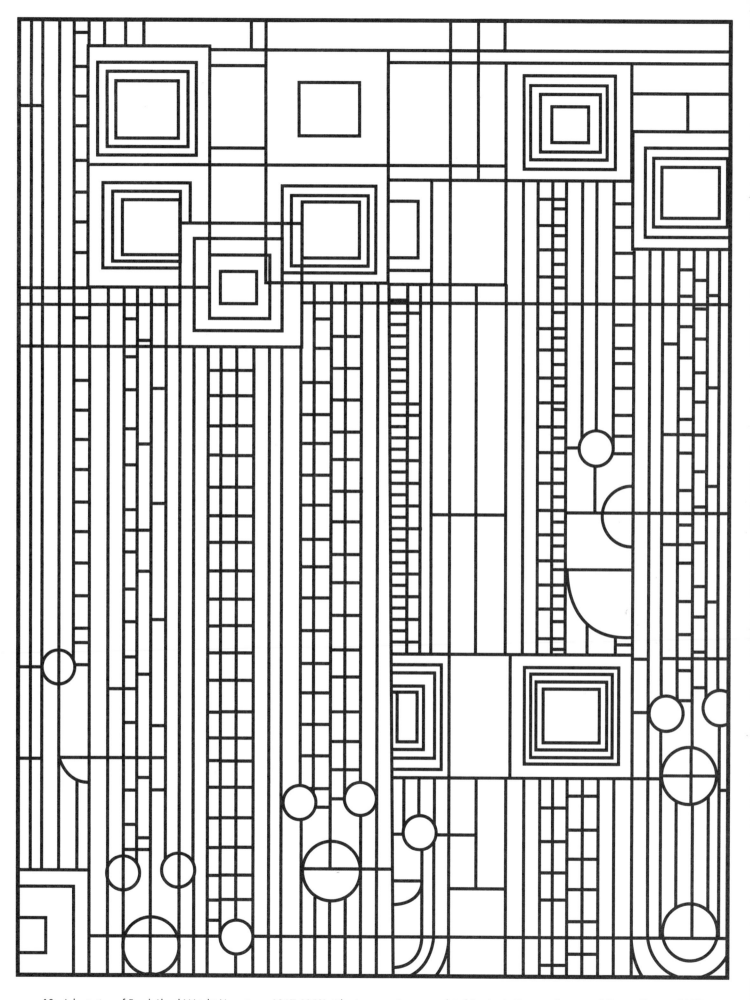

10. Adaptation of Frank Lloyd Wright (American, 1867–1959), *Liberty* magazine cover detail (project), *Saguaro Forms and Cactus Flowers*, 1927

11. Adaptation of Frank Lloyd Wright (American, 1867–1959), Mural detail, Imperial Hotel, Tokyo, Japan, 1913–1922

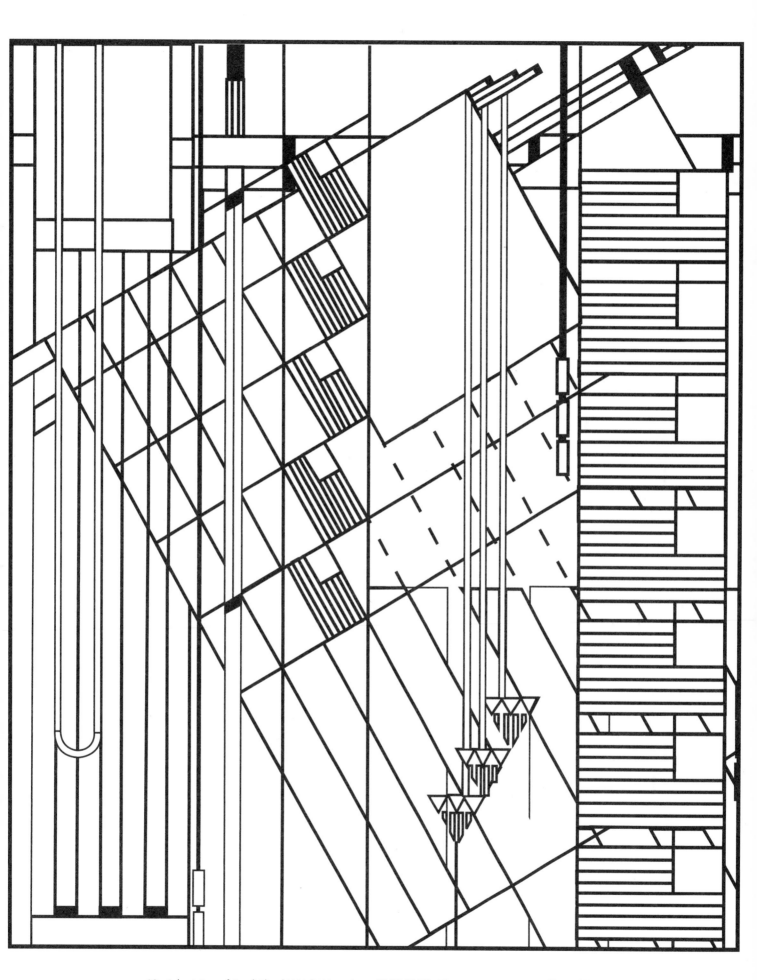

12. Adaptation of Frank Lloyd Wright (American, 1867–1959), *Liberty* magazine cover, *Flags*, 1927

13. Adaptation of Frank Lloyd Wright (American, 1867–1959), Fretwork grille detail for front door, Chauncey L. Williams House, River Forest, Illinois, 1895

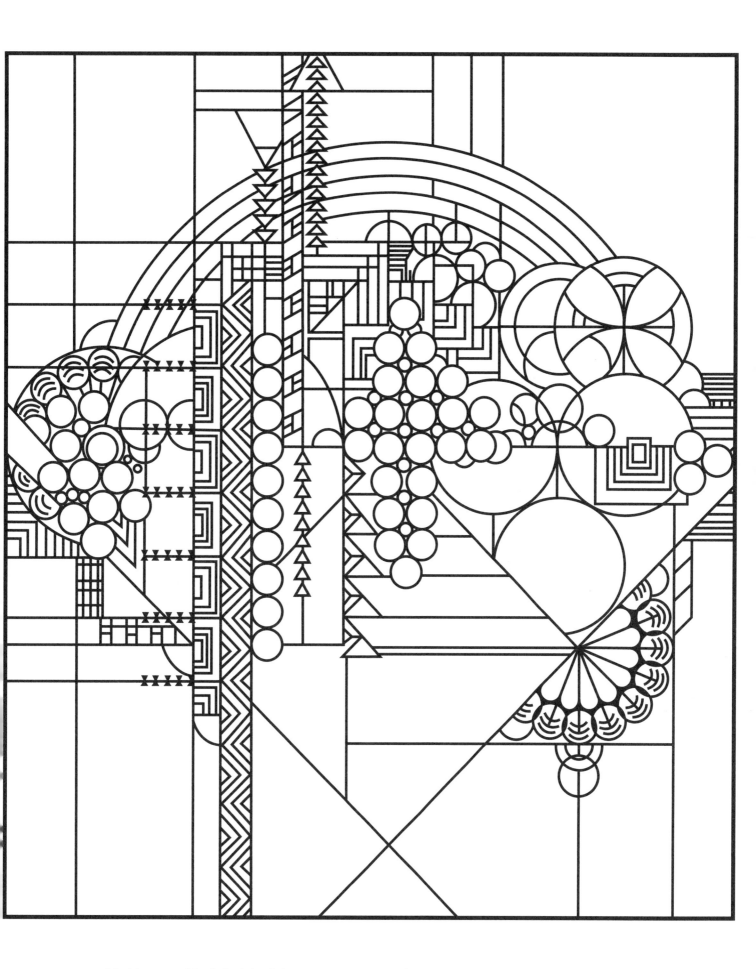

14. Adaptation of Frank Lloyd Wright (American, 1867–1959), *Liberty* magazine cover (project), *May Basket,* 1927

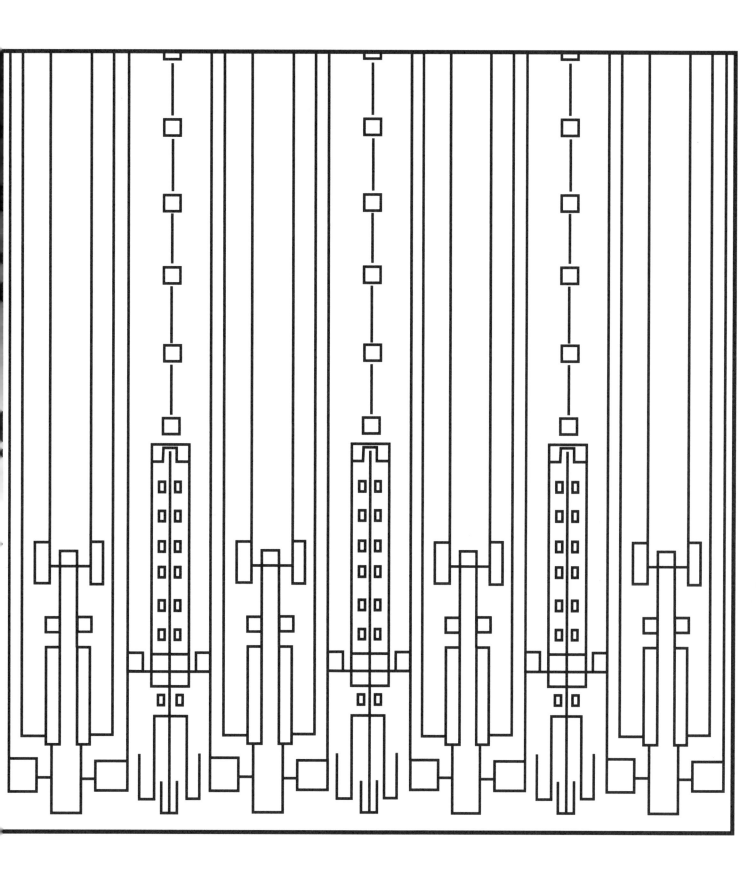

15. Adaptation of Frank Lloyd Wright (American, 1867–1959), Carpet design, Avery Coonley House, Riverside, Illinois, 1907

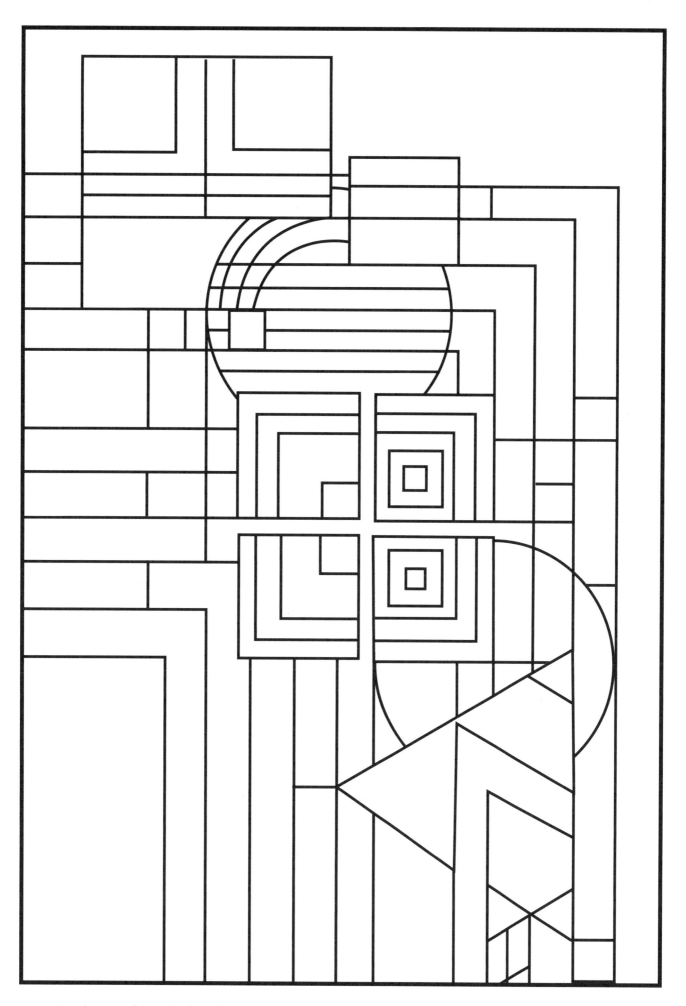

16. Adaptation of Frank Lloyd Wright (American, 1867–1959), *Liberty* magazine cover detail (project), *December Gifts*, 1927

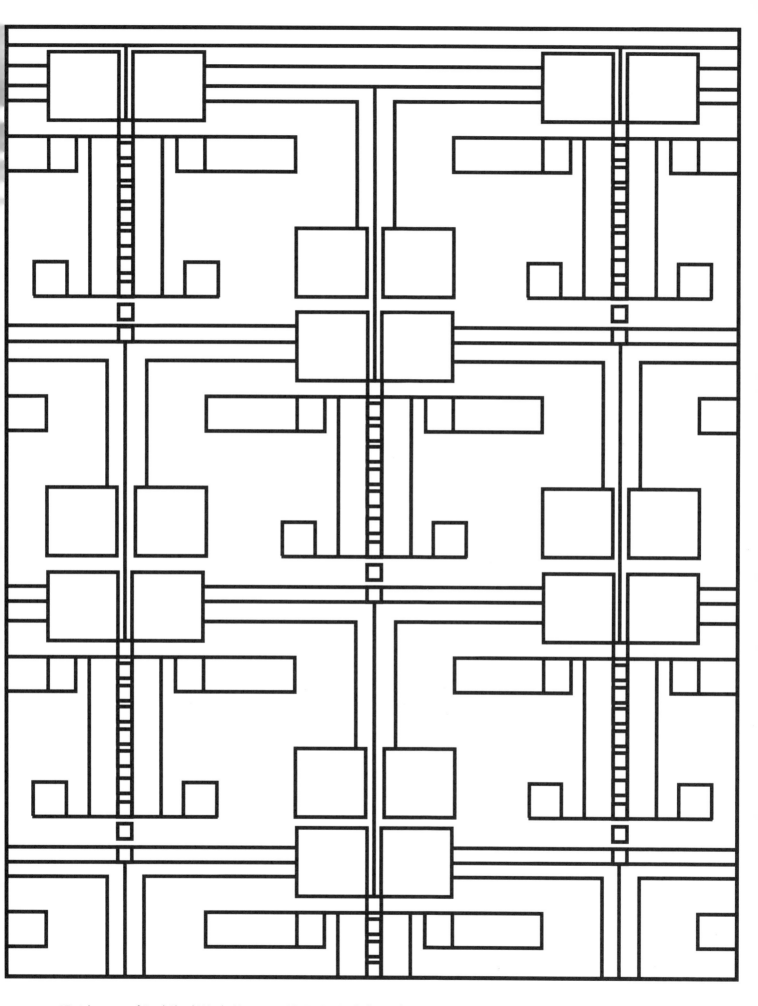

17. Adaptation of Frank Lloyd Wright (American, 1867–1959), Tile/frieze design (project), Avery Coonley House, Riverside, Illinois, 1907

18. Adaptation of Frank Lloyd Wright (American, 1867–1959), *Liberty* magazine cover (project), *Frozen Spheres*, 1927

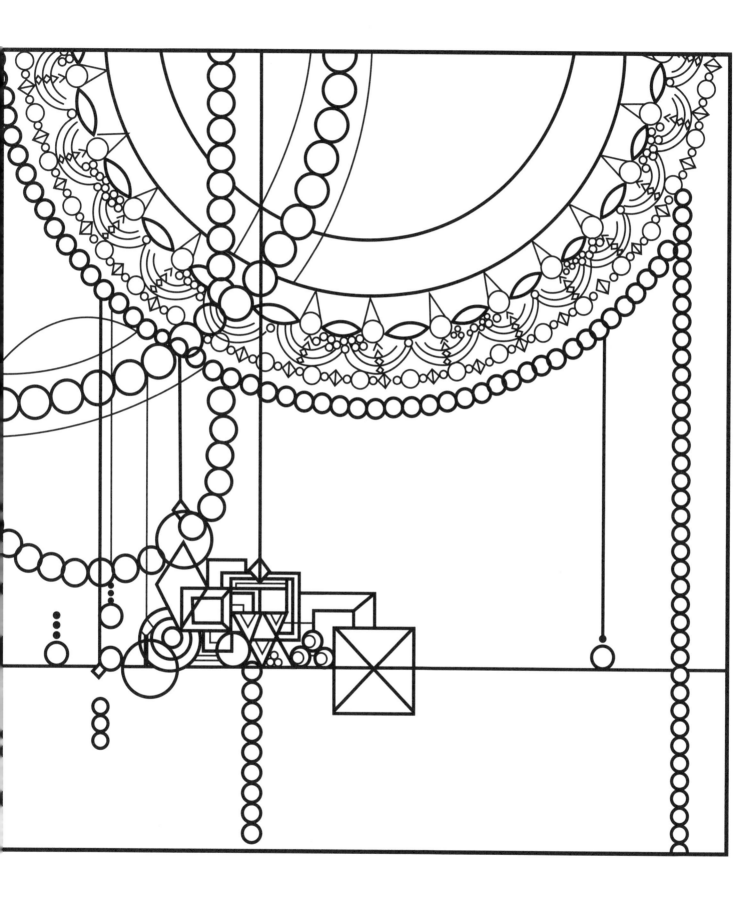

19. Adaptation of Frank Lloyd Wright (American, 1867–1959), *Liberty* magazine cover (project), *Jewelry Shop Window*, 1927

20. Adaptation of Frank Lloyd Wright (American, 1867–1959), Fretwork grille detail for front door, Nathan Moore House, Oak Park, Illinois, 1923

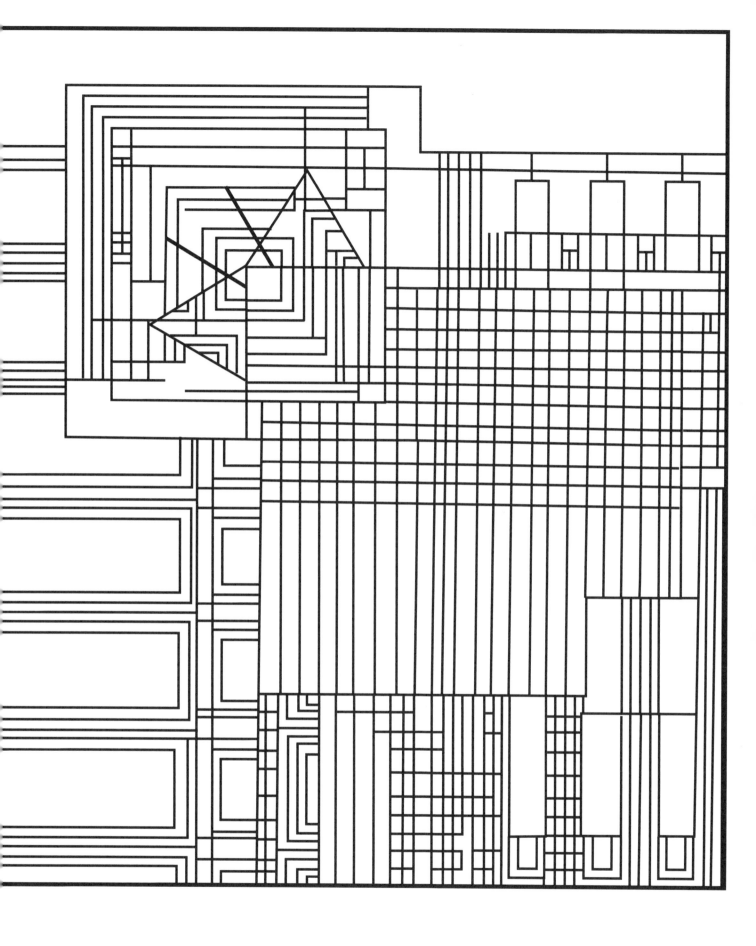

21. Adaptation of Frank Lloyd Wright (American, 1867–1959), *Liberty* magazine cover detail (project), *Old-Fashioned Window*, 1927

22. Adaptation of Frank Lloyd Wright (American, 1867–1959), Metal altar screen detail, Annunciation Greek Orthodox Church, Wauwatosa, Wisconsin, 1956

Draw and color your own picture here!